The Best of More Music To Watch Girls By

Production: Sadie Cook and Ulf Klenfeldt

Cover artwork used by permission of Sony Music Entertainment (UK) Ltd

Published 1999

IMP

International
MUSIC
Publications

International Music Publications Limited
Griffin House 161 Hammersmith Road London W6 8BS England

Anyone Who Had A Heart

Words by Hal David
Music by Burt Bacharach

The Best Is Yet To Come

Words by Carolyn Leigh
Music by Cy Coleman

Can't Help Falling In Love

Words and Music by
George Weiss, Hugo Peretti and Luigi Creatore

Born Free

Words by Don Black
Music by John Barry

Casino Royale
(Have No Fear Bond Is Here)

Words by Hal David
Music by Burt Bacharach

Though he's a lov-er, when ___ you are in trou-ble have no fear. Look who's,

here: James Bond. ___ They've got us on the

run with guns ___ and knives. ___ We're

fight-ing for our lives. Have no fear Bond is here,

He's gon-na save the world. Bond is here have no fear!

Fade

Cast Your Fate To The Wind

Music by
Vince Guaraldi

EMI Music Publishing Ltd, London WC2H 0EA

Fever

Words and Music by
John Davenport and Eddie Cooley

Verse 3 Romeo loved Juliet
Juliet she felt the same,
When he put his arms around her, he said,
"Julie, baby you're my flame."

Chorus Thou givest fever, when we kisset'
Fever with my flaming youth,
Fever – I'm afire
Fever, yea I burn forsooth.

Verse 4 Captain Smith and Pocahantas
Had a very mad affair,
When her Daddy tried to kill him, she said,
"Daddy-o don't you dare."

Chorus Give me fever, with his kisses,
Fever when he holds me tight.
Fever – I'm his Missus
Oh Daddy won't you treat him right.

Verse 5 Now you've listened to my story
Here's the point that I have made:
Chicks were born to give you fever
Be it fahrenheit or centigrade.

Chorus They give you fever when you kiss them,
Fever if you live and learn.
Fever – till you sizzle
What a lovely way to burn.

Guaglione

Music by
Fanciulli and Nisa

Tempo di Cha-cha

From Russia With Love

Words and Music by Lionel Bart
Arranged by John Barry

Look Of Love

Words by Hal David
Music by Burt Bacharach

Verse 2:
You've got the look of love, it's on your face,
A look that time can't erase.
Be mine tonight, let this be just the start
Of so many nights like this;
Let's take a lover's vow
And then seal it with a kiss.

I can hardly wait *etc.*

Verse 3: (Instrumental)

I can hardly wait *etc.*

If You Go Away (Ne Me Quitte Pas)

Words and Music by
Jaques Brel

The More I See You

Words by Mack Gordon
Music by Harry Warren

'S Wonderful

Music and Lyrics by
George Gershwin and Ira Gershwin

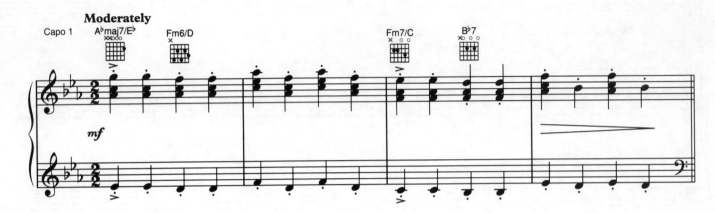

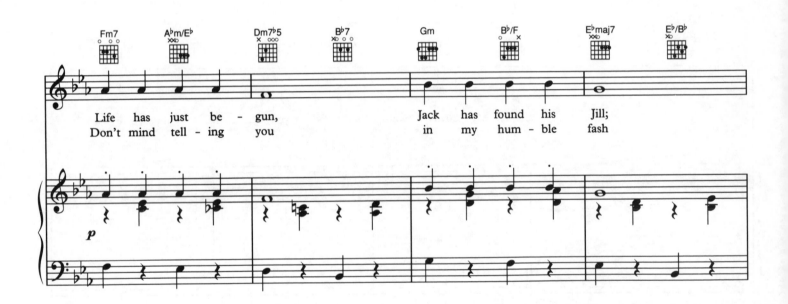

Life has just be - gun,   Jack has found his Jill;
Don't mind tell - ing you   in my hum - ble fash

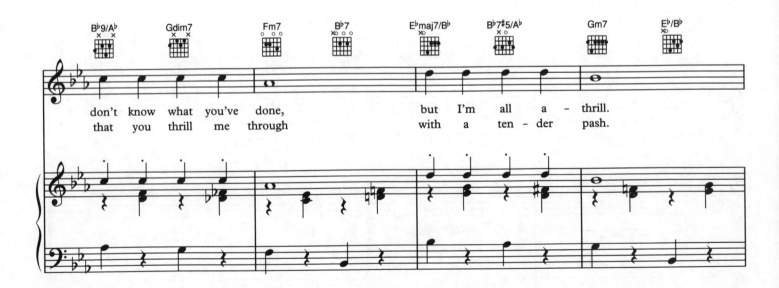

don't know what you've done,   but I'm all a - thrill.
that you thrill me through   with a ten - der pash.

What A Difference A Day Made

Spanish Words and Music by Maria Grever
English Words by Stanley Adams

The Windmills Of Your Mind

Words by Alan and Marilyn Bergman
Music by Michel Legrand

What A Wonderful World

Words and Music by
George David Weiss and Bob Thiele

Printed in England
The Panda Group · Haverhill · Suffolk · 12/99